The 7 Habits Family Journal

Foreword by Stephen R. Covey

Quotes from *The 7 Habits of Highly Effective Families*

FranklinCovey™

Also by Stephen R. Covey:
The 7 Habits of Highly Effective Families
The 7 Habits of Highly Effective People
Principle-Centered Leadership
First Things First, with A. Roger Merrill and Rebecca R. Merrill

For a catalog or additional information about Franklin Covey
products and services, call 1-800-654-1776. You can also visit
the Franklin Covey web site at www.franklincovey.com.

This journal is printed on acid-free, archival-quality paper.

Foreword

OF ALL THE INNER GIFTS unique to human beings, the most unique is self-awareness—the ability to "step outside ourselves" and reflect on our thinking, our behavior, our strengths and weaknesses, and our motives. As I have taught and led programs around the world, I have asked thousands of people: "Of all the unique human gifts—particularly conscience, imagination, independent will, and self-awareness—which one do you struggle with the most?" Their answer is always self-awareness.

One of the best ways I know to nurture self-awareness as a family is to keep a journal. Writing in a family journal offers a source of belonging—of identity. Children, both young and old, will find a family journal a great source of comfort and security. It helps them know they belong and are part of something beautiful. It also helps them understand that their family creates a uniquely safe environment in which they can grow and develop. I suggest that you keep a personal journal for recording your private thoughts and a family journal for helping create unity and an identity within your family.

How can a family begin to keep a family journal? I suggest that you start by developing a family mission statement that identifies the kind of family you want to be six months from now, a year from now, and beyond. Then use your family journal as a tool for keeping you close to your mission statement.

The flight of an airplane is the ideal metaphor for family life. An airplane pilot regularly checks the flight plan as the plane meets wind, rain, turbulence, and other factors that cause it to deviate off course. The pilot then makes the necessary adjustments to return to the original flight plan. A family, too, must habitually continue to correct its course if it intends to reach its destination. Keep in mind that even great families—like airplanes—are off track 90 percent of the time. All families can reach their desired destinations, which can be beautifully represented through family mission statements, by continually making course corrections.

You see, it doesn't make any difference if we are off target or even if our family is a mess. The hope lies in the vision, the plan, and the courage to keep coming back time and time again.

To keep your family's flight plan at the forefront, you may want to keep a copy of your family mission statement in the journal itself so it can be accessed every time someone uses the journal. (Pages for a family mission statement follow this foreword.)* A family journal is an ideal place for family members to express their thoughts and desires. As family members contribute to the journal, they often find that they also refine their individual and family mission statements so that they constantly reflect an accurate picture of the family's evolution.

The following ideas are a few suggestions that may make journal writing more enjoyable and meaningful for you.

Perhaps you could begin your family journal with some boundary-breaking questions. Put a list of excellent, thought-provoking questions somewhere in the family journal so there is always a subject available to write about.

Just as Anne Frank named her now-famous journal "Kitty," you too can name your journal. Make it a meaningful name. For example, if the family is planning a family reunion together in two years, name the journal "Reunion." It will serve as a reminder to the family of what they have to look forward to. Remember that the anticipation of an event is just as rewarding as the event itself.

Parents can also use a section in the family journal for each child. While parents and grandparents enjoy looking back at a child's first words, first foods, and more, it's probably even more enjoyable for the child. All of us enjoy hearing what we were like as children, and having a written record of our childhood is priceless. Often parents think they will remember all of the wonderful things their children did, but the memories fade with time. When all of the information is compiled in a single written source, it can be a source of comfort, strength, and love for years to come. And what a wonderful gift a compilation of childhood memories would make to give a son or daughter on his or her wedding day. The journal would serve as a powerful link not only between a young man or young woman's childhood and adulthood, but also between newlyweds and their future family.

* If you would like some examples of mission statements or a worksheet to help you develop a family mission statement, please call 1-800-654-1776.

What could you capture in a family journal? The possibilities are endless. Politics, current events, poetry, music, art, and goals are certain to stimulate thought and discussion. You can place drawings, programs or tickets, photographs, and other mementoes or reminders on the blank pages in the journal.

You can also use your family journal as a reminder of particular events the family experienced—a vacation or even a funeral, for example. Writing it down solidifies the event and helps you take a snapshot of moments you'll likely be able to reflect on as a family for years to come.

While each family member should write what he or she feels comfortable with, it is equally important that difficult issues are not ignored. Instead, use the journal as a tool for working out those deep thoughts and emotions.

Keeping a journal is a powerful and precious way of leaving a legacy to your family or loved ones. Future generations can learn from your family's experiences, struggles, private victories, and efforts to grow and overcome the challenges of life. Most of us underestimate the value of what such a record could someday mean to other people. A family journal opens up a window to your family's soul. In that window, people will come to see your family as a beautiful family unit through your hopes, your dreams, your convictions, your strengths, and your heartaches. By creating this powerful bond with your family, they can then find new hope and courage for their own lives.

I wish you all the best in your journey.

Stephen R. Covey

Mission Statement

Journal

The key is in having a destination, a flight plan, and a compass. (p. 10)

People do not see the world as it is; they see it as they are. (p. 203)

_____

Habit 1—Be Proactive—is the ability to act based on principles and values rather than reacting based on emotion or circumstance. (p. 29)

_____

No matter what the situation, there are always things you can do that will make relationships better. (pp. 46–47)

There are certain fundamental principles that govern in all human interactions, and living in harmony with those principles...is absolutely essential for quality family life. (p. 15)

The reality [is] that all true and lasting change occurs from the inside out. (p. 15)

Just smile and keep moving forward. (p. 22)

[Humor] is vitally important to the development of a beautiful family culture. (p. 33)

Twelve hugs a day—that's what people need. Hugs come physically, verbally,
visually, environmentally. (p. 51)

One of the most important deposits an individual can make...is to be loyal to family members when they are not present. (p. 55)

It isn't the snake bite that does the serious damage; it's chasing the snake that drives the poison to the heart. (p. 61)

_____

_____

_____

_____

_____

_____

_____

_____

_____

_____

_____

_____

_____

_____

_____

_____

_____

_____

_____

_____

_____

_____

_____

_____

The truth is that the basic solutions to our problems lie within us. (p. 66)

_____

_____

_____

_____

_____

_____

_____

_____

_____

_____

_____

_____

_____

_____

_____

_____

_____

_____

_____

_____

_____

_____

Mission statements focus on possibilities, not on limitations. (p. 90)

Love is a verb. It's also a commitment. (p. 99)

The process is as important as the product. (p. 81)

No involvement, no commitment. (p. 89)

In the end, life teaches us what is important, and that is family. (p. 116)

_____

_____

_____

_____

_____

_____

_____

_____

_____

_____

_____

_____

_____

_____

_____

_____

_____

_____

_____

_____

_____

_____

_____

_____

Win-win is really the only solid foundation for effective family interaction…
[it] builds long-term relationships of trust and unconditional love. (p. 179)

You cannot hold people responsible for results if you supervise their methods. (p. 192)

_____

Each person needs to be loved in his or her own special way. The key...therefore, is to understand—and to speak—that person's language of love. (p. 214)

One-on-ones are where most of the real work of the family is done. This is where there is the deepest nurturing of heart and soul. (p. 152)

_If we do not teach our children, society will. And they—and we—will live with
the results._ (p. 146)

_____

_____

_____

_____

_____

_____

_____

_____

_____

_____

_____

_____

_____

_____

_____

_____

_____

_____

_____

_____

_____

_____

_____

_____

To those who would say, "We don't have time to do these things!" I would say, "You don't have time not to!" (p. 163)

What is important to another person must be as important to you as the other person is to you. (p. 179)

Abundance Mentality is the spirit of "family." It's the spirit of "we." (p. 181)

Synergy is creative *teamwork*, creative *cooperation*. (p. 258)

Without understanding, you might as well be yelling into the wind. (p. 203)

One of the best parts of being a family is that you can encourage one another.
You can believe in one another. You can affirm one another. (p. 358)

When you understand, you don't judge. (p. 208)

_____

_____

_____

_____

_____

_____

_____

_____

_____

_____

_____

_____

_____

_____

_____

_____

_____

_____

_____

Creating a warm, caring, supportive, encouraging environment is probably the most important thing you can do for your family. (p. 216)

[Families] become more unified and connected as they join together in a sacred
expression of things that are important to them. (p. 279)

_____

_____

_____

_____

_____

_____

_____

_____

_____

_____

_____

_____

_____

_____

_____

_____

_____

_____

_____

_____

_____

_____

_____

_____

It's the diversity that creates the interest, the flavor, the new combination that puts together the best of all different things. (p. 257)

Family itself is a "we" experience, a "we" mentality. (p. 20)

In relationships the little things are the big things. (p. 51)

Every family must take time to renew itself in the four key areas of life: physical,
social, mental, and spiritual. (p. 277)

_____

The way you treat any relationship in the family will eventually affect every relationship in the family. (p. 56)

Keep in mind that when you're working with your family, "slow" is "fast" and "fast" is "slow." (p. 22)

You cannot not model. It's impossible. People will see your example—positive or negative—as a pattern for the way life is to be lived. (p. 327)